Name: _____

Habits of a Successful Middle School Musician

PERCUSSION

A Comprehensive Method Book for Years Two, Three, and Beyond

SCOTT RUSH
JEFF SCOTT • EMILY WILKINSON
RICH MOON • KEVIN BOYLE
EDITED BY MARGUERITE WILDER

Available Editions:

Flute	G-9142
Oboe	G-9143
Bassoon	G-9144
Clarinet	G-9145
Bass Clarinet	G-9146
Alto Saxophone	G-9147
Tenor Saxophone	G-9148
Baritone Saxophone	G-9149
Trumpet	G-9150
French Horn	G-9151
Trombone	G-9152
Euphonium	G-9153
Baritone TC	G-9154
Tuba	G-9155
Mallets	G-9156
Percussion	G-9157
Conductor's edition	G-9158

GIA PUBLICATIONS, INC.
CHICAGO

Habits of a Successful Middle School Musician – Percussion Edition
Scott Rush • Jeff Scott • Emily Wilkinson • Rich Moon • Kevin Boyle

G-9157
ISBN: 978-1-62277-194-3

Contents

Welcome to the *Habits of a Successful Musician* series. This supplemental method book was written to help you establish an effective daily routine that will ultimately lead to great music making. As you perfect the various components of playing, it is important that they only serve as a means to an end, for being the chance to call your performances *artistic*.

This method book is primarily a warm-up, chorale, rhythm and sight-reading curriculum. Each exercise has a very specific purpose. However, once these skills have been mastered, the technique of playing must logically progress to more musical concepts. Let's begin our musical journey!

Many times our warm-up methods and exercises are wonderful for our brass and woodwind students, but the percussion applications of those exercises are stretched, and at times not applicable at all. This portion of the *Habits of a Successful Middle School Musician* was developed with this in mind.

The exercises contained in this book have been compiled and edited from the standard resources for percussion warm-up material. They give the student and director a sequenced series of exercises for each section of the wind book. These exercises, when played correctly, will allow the middle school percussionist of all levels to improve daily.

Rudiments Covered in this book

Rudiments are the "scales" of the snare drum. When these "scales" are mastered, the percussion student can perform proficiently on any non-mallet instrument, just as the wind player can perform melodic studies.

The Scale and Arpeggio Exercises section of the Warm-Up incorporate the following 17 rudiments in a sequential order:

Single-Stroke Roll	Flam Accent
5-Stroke Roll (open and closed)	Flam Paradiddle
7-Stroke Roll (open and closed)	Flamacue
9-Stroke Roll (open and closed)	Drag (ruff)
Single-Paradiddle	Drag-Tap
Double-Paradiddle	Single-Ratamacue
Triple-Paradiddle	Double-Ratamacue
Flam	Triple-Ratamacue
Flam-Tap	

There are 7 major scales covered in this book, each with 4 patterns (a., b., c., d.).
The percussion scale exercises are INTERCHANGABLE with ALL 7 SCALES.

Timpani

Despite their rich history, the timpani are the most under-utilized percussion instrument in the daily warm-up.

Since only one student can use them at a time, and the nature of this instrument is so unique, the Conductor's Edition Appendices address the tuning process, mallet technique, playing area, and dampening, so that these drums can be used daily in an educational and musical way in the warm-up routine.

Timpani exercises are included in the Articulation, Chord Progressions, and Chorale exercises of this book, and progress in a logical sequence to ensure the musical growth of the young percussionist. Please consult page 66 for basic percussion tips.

I. Warm-Up

1. Stretching and Flexibility

2. Interval Studies - Snare Drum

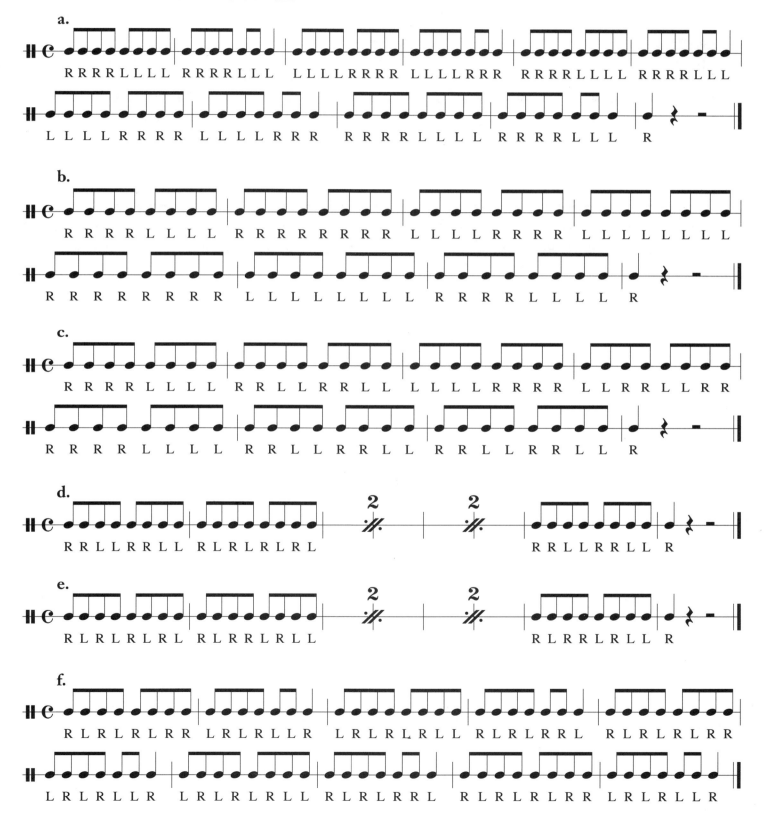

g.

R R L L R R L L R R L L R R L L L R R L L R R L L R R L L R R L L R R L L R

R L L R R L L L R R L L R R L L R R L L R R R L L R R L L R R L L R R L L

h.

R L L L R L L L R L L L R L L L R L L L R L L L R L L L L L R

i.

L R R R L R R R L R R R L R R R L R R R L R R R L R R R R R L

3.   Whole Tone Scale

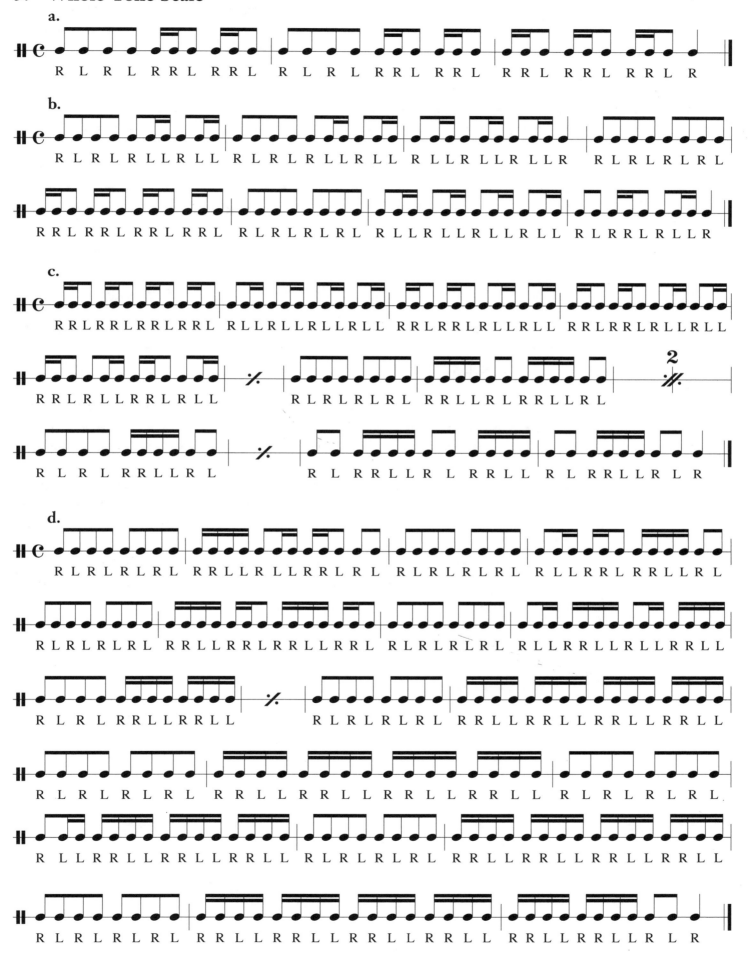

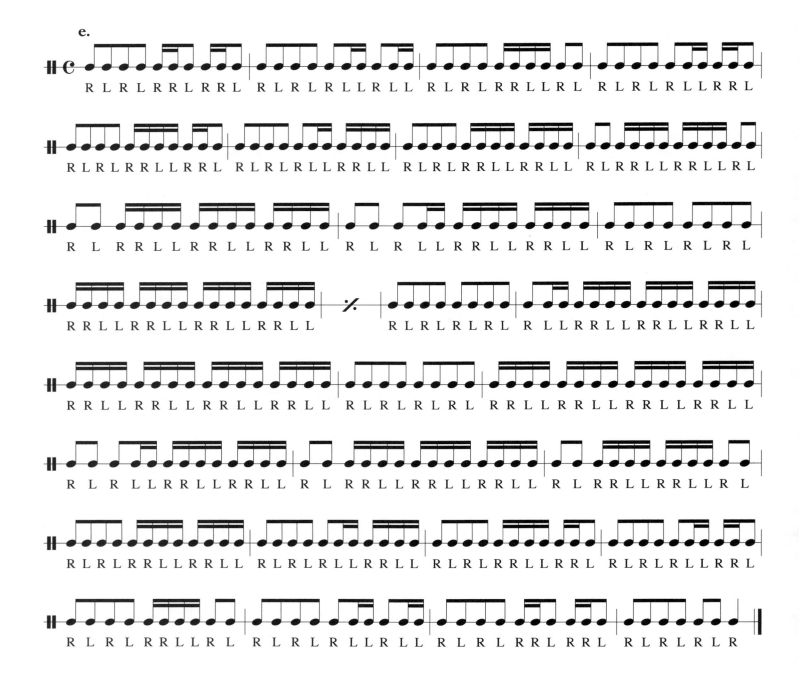

4.   **Attack Pattern** - Mallets

a. **Balance, Blend, Tuning, Tone**

5. Scale and Arpeggio Studies - Snare Drum
a. B♭ Scale

Flams

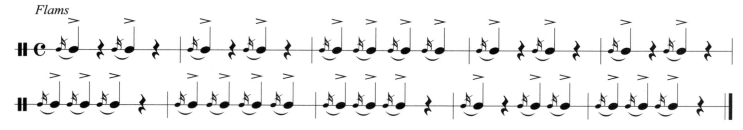

(Use the following sticking combinations)

Right-Hand Flams   Left-Hand Flams

Alternating Flams

b. *Flam Taps*

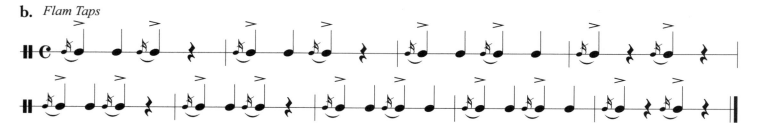

(Use the following sticking combinations)

Right-Hand lead Flam Taps

Left-Hand lead Flam Taps

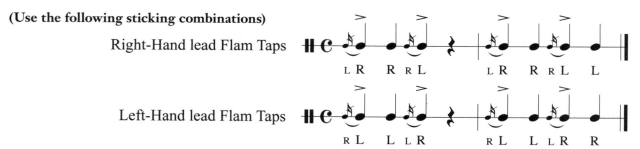

c.

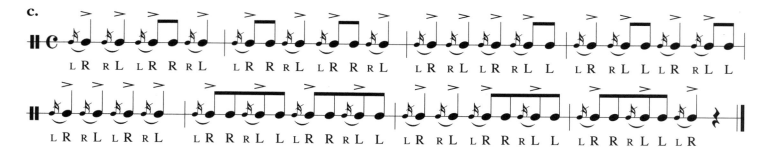

d. B♭ Scale

Major Scale

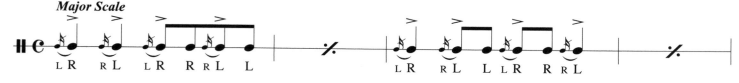

I. Warm-Up

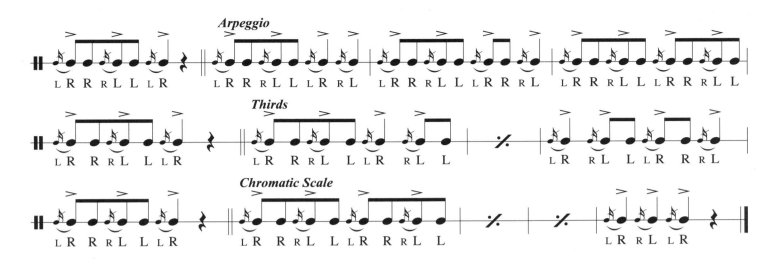

a. E♭ Scale

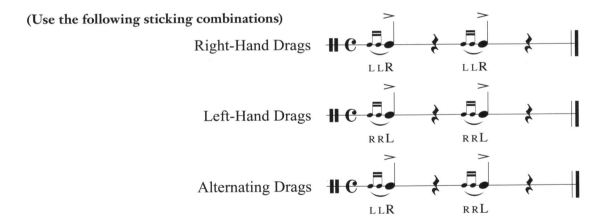

(Use the following sticking combinations)

Right-Hand Drags

Left-Hand Drags

Alternating Drags

b. *Single Drag-Taps - No accents on these drags*

(Use the following sticking combinations)

Right-Hand lead Drag Taps

Left-Hand lead Drag Taps

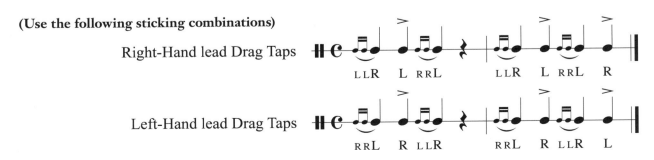

This page intentionally left blank

c.

d. E♭ Scale

Major Scale

Arpeggio

Thirds

Chromatic Scale

a. A♭ Scale - Single, Double, and Triple Paradiddles

b.

c.

d. A♭ Scale

Major Scale

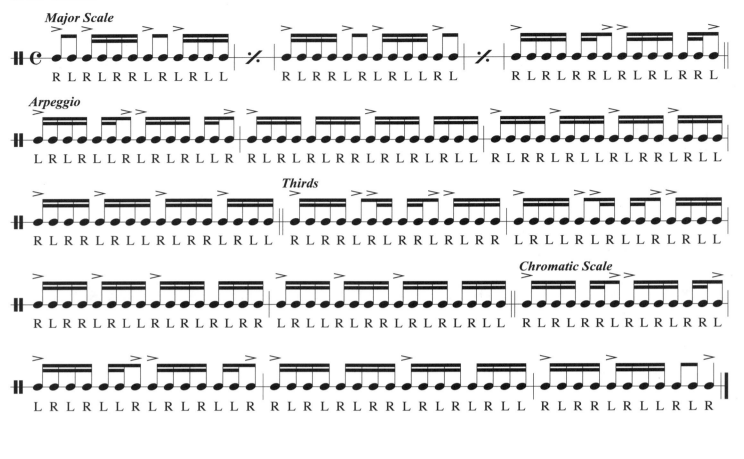

R L R L R R L R L R L L   R L R R L R L R L L R L   R L R L R R L R L R L R R L

Arpeggio

L R L R L L R L R L R L L R   R L R L R L R R L R L R L R L L   R L R R L R L L R L R L R R L R L L

Thirds

R L R R L R L L R L R R L R L L   R L R R L R L R R L R L R R   L R L L R L R L L R L R L L

Chromatic Scale

R L R R L R L L R L R L R L R R   L R L L R L R R L R L R L R L L   R L R L R R L R L R L R L R R L

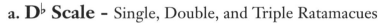

L R L R L L R L R L R L L R   R L R L R L R R L R L R L R L L   R L R R L R L L R L R

a. D♭ Scale – Single, Double, and Triple Ratamacues

No accents on these drags

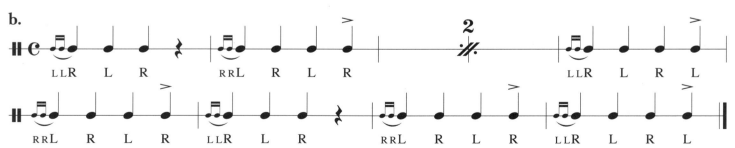

L L R   R   R R L   R   L   R   L L R   L   R   L

R R L   R   L   R   L L R   R   R R L   R   L   R

b.

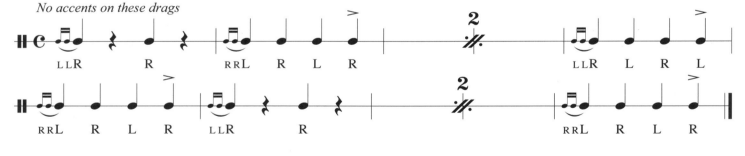

L L R   L   R   R R L   R   L   R   L L R   L   R   L

R R L   R   L   R   L L R   L   R   R R L   R   L   R   L L R   L   R   L

c.

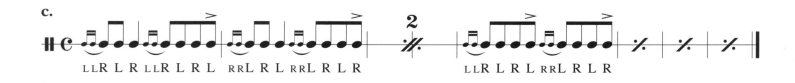

L L R L R L L R L R L   R R L R L R R L R L R   L L R L R L R R L R L R

d. D♭ Scale

a. G Scale

b.

c.

d. G Scale – 5-, 7-, 9-, and 13-Stroke Rolls (closed)

Major Scale

Arpeggio

Thirds

Chromatic Scale

a. C Scale - Flam Paradiddles and Flamacues

L R L R ʀ L R L   L R L R ʀ L R L   L R R ʀ L L L   L R R ʀ L L L   L R L R R ʀ L

L R L R R ʀ L   L R   ʀ L R L L   L R   ʀ L R L L   L R L R R ʀ L R L L   L R L R R ʀ L

b.

No accents on these flams

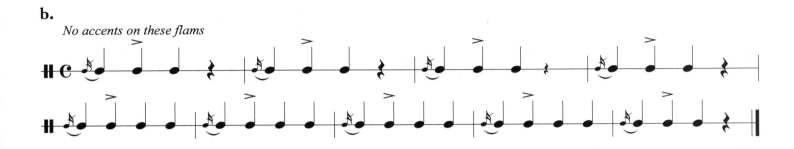

(Use the following sticking combinations)

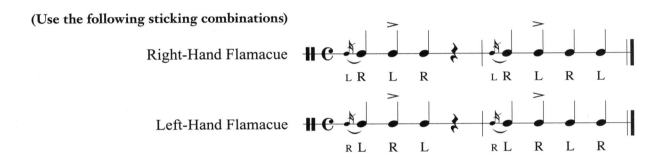

Right-Hand Flamacue

ʟ R   L   R   ʟ R   L   R   L

Left-Hand Flamacue

ʀ L   R   L   ʀ L   R   L   R

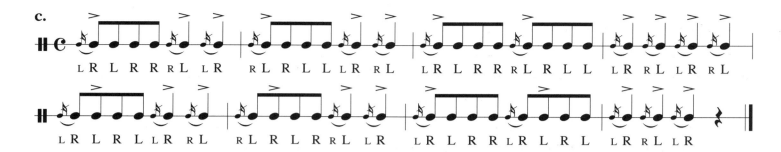

c.

d. C Scale

Major Scale

Arpeggio

Thirds

Chromatic Scale

(Use the following sticking combinations)

L R R L L R L R R R L L R R L R L R L L L R R L L R L R L R L L R L L R R L R L R

a. F Scale - *Flam Accents*

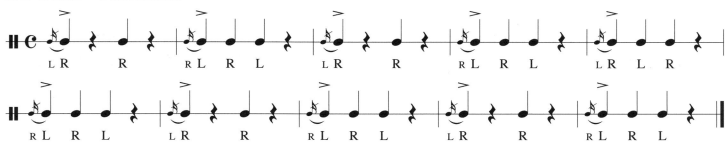

b.

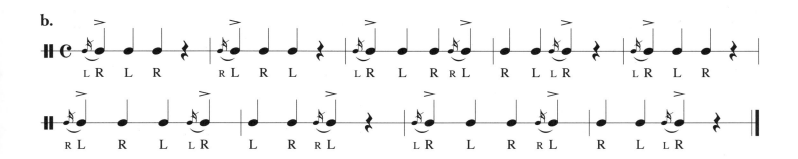

c.

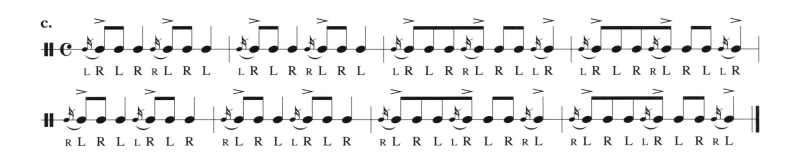

d. F Scale

Major Scale

Arpeggio

Thirds

Chromatic Scale

6. Lip Slur Exercises (B = Both hands at the same time; avoid flamming)

a.

b.

c.

RRRRRRR RRRRR   LLLLLLL LLLLL   RRRRRRR RRRRR

LLLLLLL LLLLL   RRRRRRR RRRRR   LLLLLLL LLLLL

RRRRRRR RRRRR   LLLLLLL LLLLL   BBBBBBB BBBBB

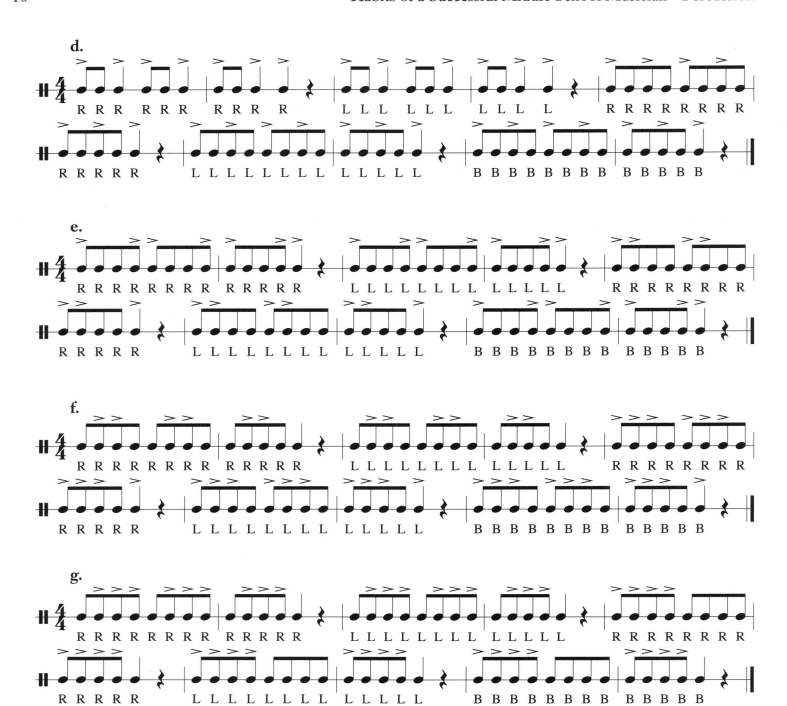

h.

7. Articulation Exercises - Timpani

a.

TUNING: B♭-F

b.

TUNING: B♭-F

c.

TUNING: B♭-F

d.

TUNING: B♭-F

14 a

g.

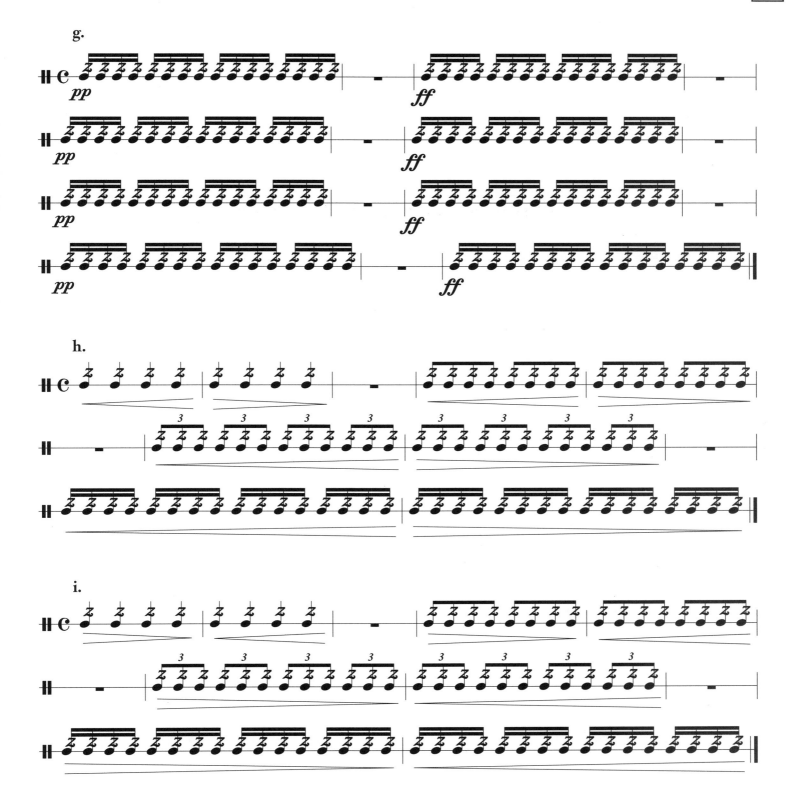

h.

i.

This page intentionally left blank

9. Chord Progression - Timpani

a.
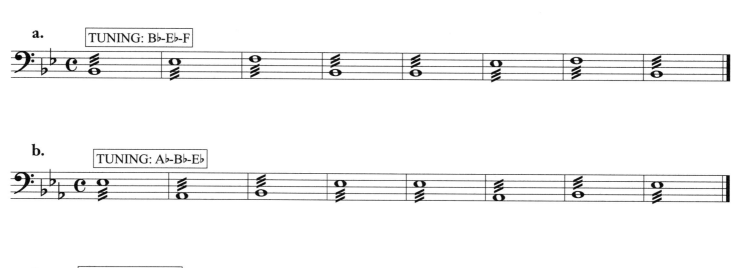

b.

c.

d.

e.

f.

g.

II. Chorales
Timpani

Chorale #1

Chorale #2

Chorale #3

Chorale #4

Chorale #5

Chorale #6

Chorale #7

Chorale #8

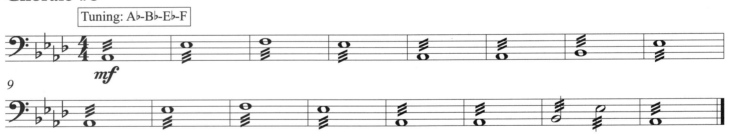

Chorale #9

Chorale #10

Chorale #11

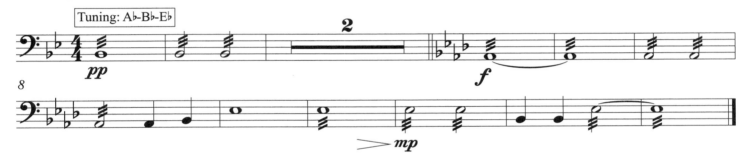

Chorale #12

Chorale #13

Chorale #14

Chorale #15

III. Rhythm Vocabulary
Mallets

10a.

10b.

11a.

11b.

11c.

22a.

22b.

23a.

23b.

24a.

24b.

25a.

25b.

29a.

29b.

30a.

30b.

31a.

31b.

32a.

32b.

33a.

33b.

39a.

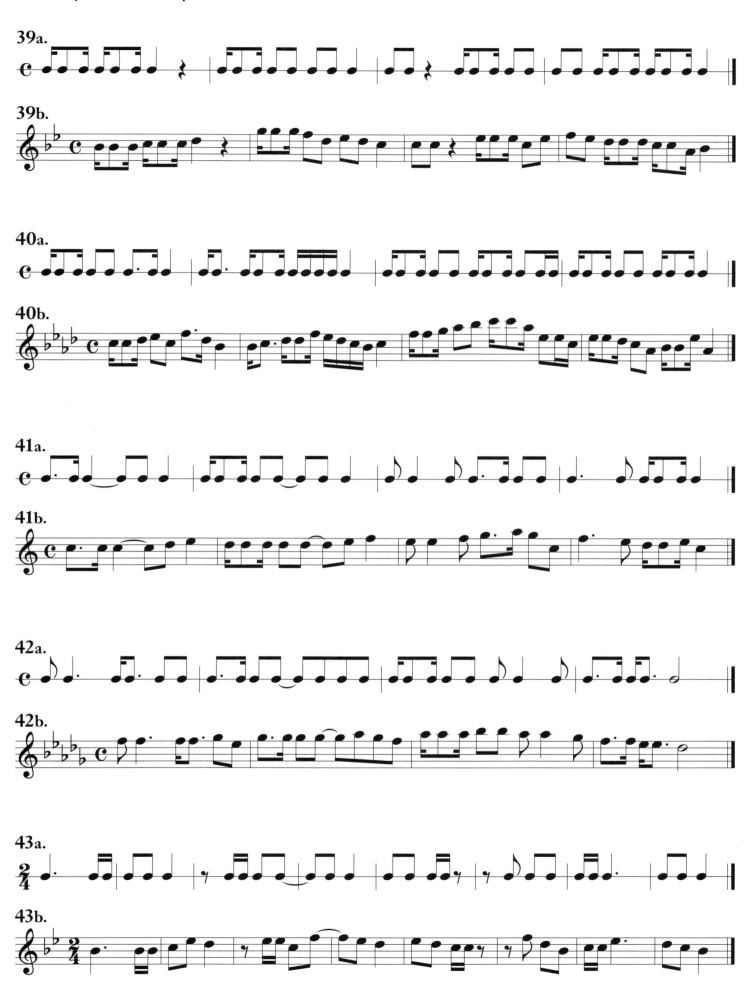

39b.

40a.

40b.

41a.

41b.

42a.

42b.

43a.

43b.

44a.

44b.

45a.

45b.

46a.

46b.

47a.

47b.

48a.

48b.

49a.

49b.

50a.

50b.

51a.

51b.

52a.

52b.

53a.

53b.

54a.

54b.

55a.

55b.

56a.

56b.

57a.

57b.

58a.

58b.

IV. Sight-Reading by Level
Mallets

You will notice that section four has very few annotated dynamics or articulations. This was done to allow the concepts of *timing* and *pulse* to be the primary focus while sight-reading in this section. Other "components of playing" will be added in section five.

17.

18.

19.

20.

21.

22.

23.

24.

25.

63.

64.

65.

66.

67.

68.

69.

93.

94.

95.

96.

97.

98.

99.

100.

101.

V. Audition Sight-Reading by Time Signature
Mallets

34.

105.

106.

107.

Percussion Tips

- Stay as relaxed as possible when playing.
- Make sure that both hands sound the same.
- Always play in the correct playing area on the instrument.
- Always make sure that you are using correct technique.
- Practice at home with a metronome.
- Practice in front of a mirror and make your hands Look, Feel, and Sound the same.
- Always listen to yourself and analyze what you're doing.

Timpani Tuning Process

1. Make sure that the timpani pedal is in the lowest position.
2. Hum or sing the desired pitch to yourself (use a pitch pipe).
3. Strike the drum slightly with your fingertip ONE TIME.
4. Keep your ear next to the drumhead.
5. Move the pedal up SLOWLY until it reaches the pitch.
6. Once your reach the pitch, stop pedaling; If you go too high, put the pedal back down and start over.

- Always Tune UP to the pitch.
- Tune so that no one else can hear you.
- Practice humming and singing different pitches; If you can sing it, you can play it.
- Practice tuning scale patterns on the timpani.

Timpani Playing Tips

- Strike the timpani about one third of the way between the rim and the center.
- Timpani rolls are ALWAYS played as Single-Stroke Rolls (RLRL…).
- Roll speed changes SLIGHTLY with the drum sizes:
  - Larger drums/Lower Pitches, slower speed
  - Smaller drums/Higher Pitches, faster speed
- Roll speed also changes with volume changes/dynamics.
- Softer = slower
- Louder = faster
- ALWAYS STRIVE FOR THE BEST SOUND, regardless of volume or pitch.
- Always move EFFICIENTLY when playing.
- Always listen to yourself and analyze what you're doing.

Dampening Tips (Articulation Exercises pages 11–12)

We dampen the Timpani when we don't want the sound of one drum bleeding into the other. It creates clarity in our sound, and allows us to match the "articulation" of the ensemble.

- Use your fingers to dampen, without letting go of the mallet.
- The more "flesh" that touches the drumhead, the quicker the dampening.
- You should not hear a "slap" or "contact" sound from your fingers. (This takes practice.)
- When dampening, practice using the same hand and the opposite hand to dampen the drum.
- Always dampen as close to the striking point as possible.